# KEY STAGE

## English

## KS3 Practice Papers

*Instructions, Guidance, Practice Papers & Answers*

### CONTENTS

how2become

As part of this product you have also received FREE access to online tests that will help you to pass Key Stage 3 ENGLISH *(Practice Papers).*

To gain access, simply go to:

# www.PsychometricTestsOnline.co.uk

Get more products
for passing any test at:

# www.How2Become.com

Orders: Please contact How2Become Ltd, Suite 14, 50 Churchill Square Business Centre, Kings Hill, Kent ME19 4YU.

You can order through Amazon.co.uk under ISBN: 9781911259046, via the website www.How2Become.com or through Gardners.com.

ISBN: 9781911259046

First published in 2016 by How2Become Ltd.

Copyright © 2016 How2Become.

Typeset for How2Become Ltd by Anton Pshinka.

## Disclaimer

Every effort has been made to ensure that the information contained within this guide is accurate at the time of publication. How2Become Ltd is not responsible for anyone failing any part of any selection process as a result of the information contained within this guide. How2Become Ltd and their authors cannot accept any responsibility for any errors or omissions within this guide, however caused. No responsibility for loss or damage occasioned by any person acting, or refraining from action, as a result of the material in this publication can be accepted by How2Become Ltd.

The information within this guide does not represent the views of any third party service or organisation.

# *Using your papers*

Read the instructions carefully before working through your practice papers.

*In this book, there are **two** sets of practice papers:*

**Set A** and **Set B**

Each **set** includes:

**Paper 1 – Reading**

1 hour 15 minutes **Marks out of 30**

**Paper 2 – Shakespeare**

45 minutes **Marks out of 20**

**Paper 3 – Writing**

1 hour 15 minutes **Marks out of 50**

*\*Please note, the allotted time and marks are to be used as a guideline only. They do not reflect the actual time or marks of the test.*

## Before working through the practice papers, make sure that you have the following:

- The correct testing paper;
- A blue or black pen/dark pencil;
- Rubber (optional).

## How to answer the questions:

Some of the questions in the practice papers will provide you with just an answer box, which you will need to fill in with your answer.

Be sure that your answer is **clear**.

If you write the wrong answer and wish to change it, neatly draw a cross through the incorrect answer, and write the correct answer. Make sure your answer is still written in the answer box.

| | |
|---|---|
| Wrong answer | New answer |

Some questions will require longer answers. This is indicated in two ways:

1. The number of marks the question is worth;
2. The number of lines you are given to write your answer.

_____

_____

_____

The above indicates an answer that requires more detail.

_____

The above line indicates an answer that requires few words or a simple sentence.

REMEMBER – the key thing to look out for is how many marks each question is worth. The number of marks for each question is written on the right side of each testing page.

2 marks

## Time management:

It is important that you **know the duration** of each testing paper.

Be sure to **read the front of your practice paper CAREFULLY**. This will tell you the duration of each practice paper. You can use this time limit to your advantage by estimating how long you should be spending on each question.

If you do not know the answer to one of the questions, **leave it**, and **come back** to it at the end if you have time.

If you finish before the end, go back through the paper and **check your work**.

Make sure your answers are written **clearly**.

**Cross out** any incorrect answers or anything that you do not want to be marked.

## Working through the papers:

At the end of Key Stage 3, you will be assessed in English via three papers – a **Reading** paper, a **Writing** paper, and a **Shakespeare** paper.

For the Shakespeare paper, we have provided you with a number of sample extracts for you to analyse. However, when it comes to your actual assessment, you should only answer questions in relation to the Shakespeare play you have studied in class. For the purpose of this guide, we have provided multiple extracts from three Shakespeare plays.

## How to prepare for the Reading paper:

You should spend the first 15 minutes of this exam reading through all of the extracts that are provided. The rest of the time will require you to use the information you have read, and answer questions.

- In the real test, you will not be permitted to turn over your answer booklet until the 15 minutes reading time is up. The only booklet you will have to look at is the reading material booklet.

Carefully read through the extracts. Don't rush through them – you have time, so make the most of it!

- We recommend that, while you are reading, you highlight key words and phrases which you think stand out or could be important. This will help you to locate them when it comes to answering the questions later.

The Reading paper is broken up into 3 extracts, and you will have to answer a series of questions on each one.

- Remember to divide your time up in order to accommodate all of the questions. You need to spend enough time on each extract (and set of questions), in order to make sure you finish the paper.

- We recommend that you spend approximately 20 minutes on each section. Most people tend to rush through the first set of questions, which could be costly and lose you easy marks! The key to timing is to pace yourself. Keep an eye on the clock!

Like any exam, the number of marks per question vary, and therefore we recommend that you answer the questions that award more marks first. That way, if you do run out of time, you have answered the questions that will give you four or five marks, as opposed to one or two marks.

## How to prepare for the Shakespeare paper:

Your English assessments will also include a Shakespeare section. In the classroom, you will focus on a Shakespeare play. That play will come up in the exam, amongst other plays you have not studied. **You should only answer the questions that relate to the Shakespeare play you have studied.**

However, for the purpose of this book, we have provided extracts from the following plays: *Romeo and Juliet, Othello* and *Macbeth*. Of course, you might attend a school where these plays are not taught.

Practising a variety of literary texts and getting to grips with the types of questions will only benefit you in the long run. Doing so will improve your exam technique, help you hone your essay writing, and increase your knowledge of Shakespearean literature. Practise using these questions, and then think about the types of questions that could come up about the play you have studied.

Marks will be awarded for how well you analyse the extract, and demonstrate levels of understanding and interpretation. Of course, marks will also be awarded for grammar, punctuation and spelling. Remember to use the extract to pinpoint key areas you wish to discuss. Use short, relevant quotes to highlight what you are trying to say.

## _How to prepare for the Writing paper:_

The Writing paper of the English assessment is your chance to show off your creative skills and writing ability. During this part of the exam, you will be provided with two questions – one will require a shorter written answer, and the other a longer written answer.

Although it is quite difficult to revise and prepare for the Writing paper, there are a few things that you can consider:

- The purpose of the text:
    - Are you writing to persuade, argue, entertain, give advice or describe?

- The form of the text:
    - Are you writing a story, a diary entry, a letter or a newspaper article?

- The audience of the text:
    - Who are you addressing your writing to? Is it a parent, a teacher, a head teacher or a fellow pupil?

The way in which you style your writing will depend on all of the aforementioned areas. The best way to enhance your writing ability is to practise writing with all these elements in mind – purpose, form and audience.

As mentioned, there is a short and long task. Therefore, you will need to allocate your time correctly in order to cater for this. Obviously, more time will be required for the longer writing task.

This assessment is not marking you based on how much you write. Instead, it is marking you based on the quality of your written communication. You need to ensure that everything you write is clear, accurate and relevant. It is best to write three strong and detailed paragraphs, as opposed to lots of paragraphs that are not relevant and/ or waffle on.

# *Guidance for parents*

*Welcome to your child's Key Stage 3 English Practice Papers!*

## *How to mark your child's paper:*

To determine how well your child is performing in their practice papers, use the answers at the end of each **set** to mark each practice paper. For papers Reading, Shakespeare and Writing of each set, the score will be **out of 100**.

The below tables demonstrate how you should mark your child's test papers. At the end of each set, you will be given a chance to mark the papers using the answers provided.

| | READING<br>Mark out of 30 | SHAKESPEARE<br>Mark out of 20 | WRITING<br>Mark out of 50 | TOTAL<br>Mark out of 100 |
|---|---|---|---|---|
| **SET A** | | | | |

| | READING<br>Mark out of 30 | SHAKESPEARE<br>Mark out of 20 | WRITING<br>Mark out of 50 | TOTAL<br>Mark out of 100 |
|---|---|---|---|---|
| **SET B** | | | | |

Please note that the total marks for our practice papers DO NOT reflect the actual total marks for the real testing papers. Instead, these should be used as a way of monitoring how well your child is progressing at home.

## How to monitor your child's progression:

➢ The optimum way to monitor your child's progression before their English examinations is to use practice papers to assess how much your child is improving.

➢ Although you do not want to bombard your child with testing papers, giving them a few practice papers leading up to their exams will allow them to progress at a steady speed.

➢ Instead of cramming in loads of practice a couple of weeks before your child's exam, you should try spreading these out across a few months. That way, your child will feel more relaxed, which will improve their learning over longer periods of time.

➢ Ultimately, the more practice that your child receives, the better results they will achieve in their exams.

➢ We strongly advise that you work through a practice paper with your child to find out what they struggle with. You can then work on those weaker areas to ensure they are bettered. You can test their progression by giving your child the same questions to practice with, and see whether they have learnt how to work them out. If they have, then move on to the next weak area. If not, continue working on those questions until they master them. Do this for each of their weak areas, until they feel fully competent in tackling all the questions.

## How to help your child succeed:

➢ Encourage your child to be confident in their abilities. Show them that you are proud of them.

➢ Make sure your child is getting enough sleep.

➢ Make sure they are eating balanced meals, especially for breakfast.

➢ Encourage them to ask for help at school if they are struggling with anything.

➢ Set aside pre-planned time for revision.

➢ When going through their revision booklets, make sure that your child is referring back to the text; they can gain extra marks for using direct examples from the text.

➢ Make sure that your child has everything they need for their revision (i.e. pens, paper, revision guides, etc.).

➢ Be relaxed. When your child comes home from school, ensure that their home environment is relaxed. This will reduce the pressure your child may be feeling.

➢ Allow for plenty of study breaks – even if they're 5 or 10 minutes long. This will help to refresh the memory and keep your child calm and focused. Let your child spend some time doing what they enjoy.

➢ **KEEP IN MIND** – a child's attention span is usually between 30 to 50 minutes.

➢ Active revision is a great way to stay interactive with the topic. Mock tests are great revision techniques to use to prepare for their English assessments.

➢ Visual aids are another great way to take in lots of information. Mind maps, spider diagrams, flash cards and posters should all be used in preparation.

➢ Brush up on their vocabulary. These types of tests are designed to assess your child's English and vocabulary skills. Therefore you need to be able to demonstrate a strong level of ability regarding words, phrases and meanings.

➤ Make sure your child is reading lots of different literary texts. Try to vary what kind of literature they read. For example, read classic and contemporary literature, read plays and poetry, read non-fiction texts including diary entries and letters.

➤ Practise writing. The best way to improve the fluency and effectiveness of their writing is to undergo numerous practice tasks.

➤ Sit down with your child and discuss their work with them. This will allow you to not only get an insight into what they are learning at school, but this is a great way for them to recap everything they have learnt. Speaking out loud is a great way to remember key things from the classroom.

➤ Make sure that their homework is getting done. Homework is a great way to recap everything they are learning, and therefore you will be able to see the areas they need to focus on when it comes to the exams.

➤ Try not to put too much pressure on your child. Whilst every parent wants their child to succeed, it is important not to be critical when your child gets something wrong or doesn't understand. Be supportive. Be motivated. Your child is more likely to confide in you if they feel like you are not judging them.

> We have also created other Key Stage 3 English books which provide further practice for your child's English assessments. These revision guides will guarantee your child is fully prepared for *every* aspect of the English examinations.

For more information on our Key Stage 3 books, please visit our website

# www.how2become.com

or go on to

# www.amazon.co.uk

and search 'Key Stage 3 English is Easy'

# KEY STAGE 3
# English

# SET A
# Reading
# Practice Paper 1

**Reading Material & Questions**

**1 hour 15 minutes**

| First Name | |
| --- | --- |
| Middle Name/s | |
| Last Name | |
| School | |
| Date of Birth | D D / M M / Y Y Y Y |

## Within this paper, you have three extracts:

- Alice's Adventures in Wonderland
- Enter the Magical Land of Wonder
- My Very Own Wonderland

For each extract, there are 5 questions.

There are 30 marks in total.

Make sure you pay attention to grammar, punctuation and spelling. You will be awarded marks (for the questions with multiple marks on offer) so you don't want to lose out on easy marks.

For this paper, you have 1 hour and 15 minutes. The first 15 minutes should be used to read all of the extracts. The remaining time should be used to answer the questions.

After you've finished the questions, make sure you check your answers. The answers for Set A Paper 1 can be found on pages 64 – 67.

# WONDERLAND

Alice's Adventures in Wonderland

Enter the Magical Land of Wonder

My Very Own Wonderland

Alice was beginning to get very tired of sitting by her sister on the bank, and of having nothing to do: once or twice she had peeped into the book her sister was reading, but it had no pictures or conversations in it, "and what is the use of a book," thought Alice, "without pictures or conversations?"

So she was considering in her own mind, (as well as she could, for the hot day made her feel very sleepy and stupid,) whether the pleasure of making a daisy-chain would be worth the trouble of getting up and picking the daisies, when suddenly a white rabbit with pink eyes ran close by her.

There was nothing so *very* remarkable in that; nor did Alice think it was *very* much out of the way to hear the Rabbit say to itself, "Oh dear! Oh dear! I shall be too late!" (when she thought it over afterwards, it occurred to her that she ought to have wondered at this, but at the time it all seemed quite natural); but when the Rabbit actually *took a watch out of its waistcoat-pocket*, and looked at it, and then hurried on, Alice started to her feet, for it flashed across her mind that she had never before seen a rabbit with either a waistcoat-pocket or a watch to take out of it, and, burning with curiosity, she ran across the field after it, and was just in time to see it pop down a large rabbit-hole under the hedge.

In another moment down went Alice after it, never once considering how in the world she was to get out again.

The rabbit-hole went straight on like a tunnel for some way, and then dipped suddenly down, so suddenly that Alice had not a moment to think about stopping herself before she found herself falling down what seemed to be a very deep well.

Either the well was very deep, or she fell very slowly, for she had plenty of time as she went down to look about her, and to wonder what was going to happen next. First, she tried to look down and make out what she was coming to, but it was too dark to see anything: then she looked at the sides of the well, and noticed that they were filled with cupboards and bookshelves: here and there she saw maps and pictures hung upon pegs. She took down a jar from one of the shelves as she passed; it was labelled "ORANGE MARMALADE," but to her great disappointment it was empty: she did not like to drop the jar for fear of killing somebody underneath, so managed to put it into one of the cupboards as she fell past it.

"Well!" thought Alice to herself, "after such a fall as this, I shall think nothing of tumbling down stairs! How brave they'll all think me at home! Why, I wouldn't say anything about it, even if I fell off the top of the house!" (Which was very likely true.)

*Down, down, down.* Would the fall *never* come to an end? "I wonder how many miles I've fallen by this time?" she said aloud. "I must be getting somewhere near the centre of the earth. Let me see: that would be four thousand miles down, I think –" (for, you see, Alice had learnt several things of this sort in her lessons in the schoolroom, and though this was not a *very* good opportunity for showing off her knowledge, as there was no one to listen to her, still it was good practice to say it over) "– yes, that's about the right distance – but then I wonder what Latitude or Longitude I've got to?" (Alice had not the slightest idea what Latitude was, or Longitude either, but she thought they were nice grand words to say.)

Presently she began again. "I wonder if I shall fall *through* the earth! How funny it'll seem to come out among the people that walk with their heads downwards! The Anti-pathies I think–" (she was rather glad there *was* no one listening, this time, as it didn't sound at all the right word) "– but I shall have to ask them what the name of the country is you know. Please, Ma'am, is this New Zealand or Australia?" (and she tried to curtsey as she spoke – fancy *curtseying* as you're falling through the air! Do you think you could manage it?) "And what an ignorant little girl she'll think me for asking! No, it'll never do to ask: perhaps I shall see it written up somewhere."

Down, down, down. There was nothing else to do, so Alice began talking again. "Dinah'll miss me very much to-night, I should think!" (Dinah was the cat.) "I hope they'll remember her saucer of milk at tea-time. Dinah, my dear! I wish you were down here with me! There are no mice in the air, I'm afraid, but you might catch a bat, and that's very much like a mouse, you know. But do cats eat bats, I wonder?" And here Alice began to get rather sleepy, and went on saying to herself, in a dreamy sort of way, "Do cats eat bats? Do cats eat bats?" and sometimes, "Do bats eat cats?" for, you see, as she couldn't answer either question, it didn't much matter which way she put it. She felt that she was dozing off, and had just begun to dream that she was walking hand in hand with Dinah, and was saying to her very earnestly, "Now, Dinah, tell me the truth: did you ever eat a bat?" when suddenly, thump! thump! down she came upon a heap of sticks and dry leaves, and the fall was over.

Alice was not a bit hurt, and she jumped up on to her feet in a moment: she looked up: but it was all dark overhead; before her was another long passage, and the White Rabbit was still in sight, hurrying down it. There was not a moment to be lost: away went Alice like the wind, and was just in time to hear it say, as it turned a corner, "Oh my ears and whiskers, how late it's getting!" She was close behind it when she turned the corner, but the Rabbit was no longer to be seen: she found herself in a long, low hall, which was lit up by a row of lamps hanging from the roof.

There were doors all round the hall, but they were all locked, and when Alice had been all the way down one side and up the other, trying every door, she walked sadly down the middle, wondering how she was ever to get out again.

# ENTER THE MAGICAL LAND OF WONDER

## - a Christmas like no other!

**ENJOY THE FESTIVE FUN IN THE WORLD OF WONDERLAND**

Wondering what to do for Christmas? Wondering how to spice up your Christmas? Well, look no further.

Come and see chipmunk-cheeked Santa and his reindeers in the land of snow and mistletoe.

Whether you are looking for a quick Christmas getaway, or a family day out, our magical land of wonder has something for everyone! A Christmas break for all the family to enjoy. <u>For a list of opening days and bookings, click here.</u>

## SANTA'S GROTTO

Why not come and say hello to Santa, his reindeers and his elves?

Decorated with bright lights, mistletoe and tinsel, our Santa's grotto is the most festive and vibrant place to visit this Christmas!

Unlike any other grotto, ours has been carefully crafted to provide a cosy, warm, homely feel to it. You'll be made to feel welcome and glad – get the kids involved in the Christmas spirit and party fun!

## SANTA'S TRAIL AND RUDOLPH'S RUNAWAY

Get involved in our two fun, interactive and festive walks through the forests.

Fun for the whole family, our trails will take you on a journey through our winter wonderland. Can you spot the hidden elves? Do you hear the jingle bells from Santa's sleigh?

Unwind in our log cabins, situated at the end of each trail, to warm up and relax and enjoy some quality family time.

Of course, you will receive a present for completing the trail!

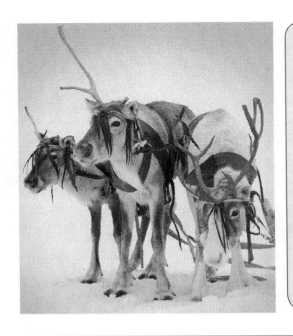

## FEED THE REINDEERS

Every child loves the idea of getting close to Santa's reindeers. Well, we are able to make this dream come true!

Why not book to feed and stroke our reindeers? Have a picture taken with them and purchase your special photo and photo frame in Santa's workshop!

To book our reindeer experience, click here.

## FUN AND FESTIVE

A hideaway place over Christmas which will guarantee to leave you feeling festive and restore childhood memories. We have something to suit everyone!

Come down to this magical winter wonderland and experience a Christmas like no other! For opening times, prices and a list of activities, click here.

10am, the air still warming,
That time of year, leaves transforming,
Colours of yellows, vibrant and gold,
A memory to share, I have never told:

A secret garden, in all its glory,
A setting for a fairy tale story.
Oh so pretty, oh so quiet;
Wildlife free, and running riot.

My feet transfixed, here I stand;
My very own wonderland.
A Garden of Eden – total perfection;
A range of flowers – a stunning collection.

1 o'clock strikes, as I look up at the sky,
I thought to myself, "Oh how I would love to fly!"
Butterflies, robins and woodpeckers surround,
Never confined to the earthy ground.

Rabbits roaming, squirrels climbing,
Picturesque, surreal, musical rhyming.
I watch the nature do its thing,
As I sit and play, and swing and swing.

The reason this place is my safe haven,
Is the freedom I feel; like a flying raven.
So strong, so powerful, so wild and free,
Traits desirable, I wish them on me.

I walk, look down, at my own reflection,
I shy away from my imperfection.
The flow of movement, calming swirl,
Liquid gold, a shining pearl.

A place of my own, where everyone is banned,
Nobody to enter my wonderland.
Filled with hope, filled with dreams,
Whether they're big, or whether extreme.

The fiery rays burning bright,
Counting the hours until moonlight.
Hours and hours have gone and passed,
My time is up, it's gone so fast.

Now the moon shines down on me,
As I sit upright under the cherry tree.
Here I sit and contemplate,
My life, my world, my unknown fate.

8 o'clock is here, and the day is over,
I feel so lucky, like a four leaf clover.
There is no place I would rather be,
A place to go, just for me.

My special place, insignificant yet grand;
To me it's the definition of a wonderland.
A place to think, a place to roam,
A place to me I'll always call home.

**Questions 1 – 5 are for *"Alice's Adventures in Wonderland"*
by Lewis Carroll (this extract can be found on page 19 – 21 of
the reading material).**

⭐**1** When Alice sits with her sister, she states how her sister's
book is boring.

Find the exact quotation Alice speaks in regards to why the book
is boring.

_____

_____

1 mark

⭐**2** Lewis Carroll depicts the character of Alice as being
conscientious.

Give two examples from the extract that demonstrates this point.

_____

_____

_____

_____

_____

_____

2 marks

⭐**3** Why do you think Carroll repeats the word "wonder"?
What does this say about the character of Alice?

_____

_____

_____

_____

1 mark

In the extract *Alice's Adventures in Wonderland*, the author uses several literary techniques in order to create meaning.

Find an example of the following, and directly quote from the extract.

**SIMILE**

**REPETITION**

**RHETORICAL QUESTION**

3 marks

How is the character of Alice portrayed in the opening extract of *Alice's Adventures in Wonderland*?

You should comment on:

- The way the author portrays Alice's character;
- The language used to create meaning and interpretation;
- Words and phrases used to highlight key themes and motifs.

3 marks

Questions 6 – 10 are for *"Enter the Magical Land of Wonder"* by How2Become (this extract can be found on pages 22 – 24 of the reading material).

**6** The author lists several reasons as to why you should visit *'The Magical Land of Wonder'*.

Give two examples of different things you can get up to during your visit.

**EXAMPLE 1**

_____

_____

**EXAMPLE 2**

_____

_____

1 mark

**7** Alliteration is used throughout this extract. Find three examples and then explain why the author might have used alliterative devices in their writing.

**EXAMPLE 1**

_____

**EXAMPLE 2**

_____

**EXAMPLE 3**

_____

**EXPLANATION**

_____

_____

_____

2 marks

**8** Does the extract persuade you to visit *'The Magical Land of Wonder'*? <u>Circle yes or no.</u>

## YES          NO

Give reasons for your answer.

_____

_____

_____

_____

_____

_____

_____

_____

_____

_____

_____

1 mark

**9** Why do you think the author begins with a question? What effect does this have on the reader?

_____

_____

_____

_____

1 mark

**10** Referring to the extract, why do you think *'The Magical Land of Wonder'* appeals to a wide group of people?

<u>You should comment on:</u>

- The language used, and the effect this has on the reader;
- The literary techniques used to create meaning;
- How the extract is persuasive and appeals to the reader.

5 marks

**Questions 11 – 15 are for *"My Very Own Wonderland"* by How2Become (this extract can be found on pages 25 – 26 of the reading material).**

 The poet of *'My Very Own Wonderland'* uses a very specific rhythmic structure.

Out of the following, which rhyming pattern replicates the rhyming pattern in the poem? <u>Tick one.</u>

**ABCA** ☐

**ABBA** ☐

**ABAB** ☐

**AABB** ☐

1 mark

Why do you think the poem uses a rhyming pattern? What effect does this have on the reader?

_____

_____

_____

_____

_____

_____

1 mark

Below is a table listing some of the literary techniques used within the poem.

For each literary technique, you need to find an example in the poem.

| LITERARY TECHNIQUE | QUOTE |
| --- | --- |
| Rhyming couplet | |
| Colour imagery | |
| Time imagery | |
| Repetition | |
| Simile | |
| Alliteration | |

2 marks

Why do you think the poet has chosen to write this poem using 1st person perspective?

_____

_____

_____

_____

_____

_____

1 mark

**14** The poet uses the phrase *"A Garden of Eden"*. What do you think this symbolises, and how is this relevant to the narrative of the poem?

_____

_____

_____

_____

_____

2 marks

**15** Within the poem, the poet often refers to time. The poem's structure has 12 stanzas. How do you think time is used in regards to the structure of the poem?

<u>You should comment on:</u>

- Why does the poet refer to time?
- Why do you think the poet has chosen to use 12 stanzas?
- What effect does this create for the reader?

_____

_____

_____

_____

_____

_____

_____

_____

_____

_____

_____

3 marks

**KEY STAGE 3**
**English**

# SET A
# Shakespeare
# Practice Paper 2

**Reading Material & Questions**
**45 minutes**

| First Name | |
|---|---|
| Middle Name/s | |
| Last Name | |
| School | |
| Date of Birth | *D D  /  M M  /  Y Y Y Y* |

## Within this paper, you have three plays:

- Romeo and Juliet
- Othello
- Macbeth

For each play, there are two extracts. There is one essay to answer based on each play.

**I would recommend you study the extracts that you are learning in the classroom**. If these are different, then practise using these to better your understanding of Shakespearean language.

There are 20 marks in total. **Answer only ONE essay question.**

Make sure you pay attention to grammar, punctuation and spelling. Your writing style will be assessed.

For this paper, you have 45 minutes. The first 15 minutes should be used to plan your essay. The remaining time should be used to write your essay.

After you've finished the questions, make sure you check your answers. The answers for Set A Paper 2 can be found on pages 68 – 70.

# SHAKESPEARE

**Romeo
and Juliet**

**Othello**

Macbeth

# Romeo and Juliet

## Act 1 Scene 5

*Romeo sees and speaks to Juliet for the very first time.*

## Act 3 Scene 5

*Juliet says goodbye to Romeo after spending the night with him.*

### ESSAY QUESTION

What themes are conveyed in these extracts? What do these themes say about the characters of Romeo and Juliet?

*Support your points by referring to both extracts.*

<u>You should comment on:</u>

- The language used
- The meaning created
- Representation
- How does Shakespeare want you as the reader to feel?

20 marks

*This extract is taken from Act 1 Scene 5 – Romeo sees and speaks to Juliet for the very first time.*

**ROMEO**

If I profane with my unworthiest hand
This holy shrine, the gentle sin is this:
My lips, two blushing pilgrims, ready stand
To smooth that rough touch with a tender kiss.

**JULIET**

Good pilgrim, you do wrong your hand too much,
Which mannerly devotion shows in this;
For saints have hands that pilgrims' hands do touch,
And palm to palm is holy palmers' kiss.

**ROMEO**

Have not saints lips, and holy palmers too?

**JULIET**

Ay, pilgrim, lips that they must use in prayer.

**ROMEO**

O, then, dear saint, let lips do what hands do;
They pray; grant thou, lest faith turn to despair.

**JULIET**

Saints do not move, though grant for prayers' sake.

**ROMEO**

Then move not, while my prayer's effect I take.
  *He kisses her*
Thus from my lips, by yours, my sin is purged.

**JULIET**

Then have my lips the sin that they have took.

**ROMEO**

Sin from thy lips? O trespass sweetly urged!
Give me my sin again.
  *They kiss again*

**JULIET**

You kiss by the book.

**NURSE**

Madam, your mother craves a word with you.

**ROMEO**

What is her mother?

**NURSE**

Marry, bachelor,

Her mother is the lady of the house,

And a good lady, and a wise and virtuous:

I nursed her daughter, that you talkt withal;

I tell you, he that can lay hold her

Shall have the chinks.

**ROMEO**

Is she a Capulet?

O dear account! My life is my foe's debt.

**BENVOLIO**

Away, be gone; the sport is at the best.

**ROMEO**

Ay, so I fear; the more is my unrest.

**CAPULET**

Nay, gentlemen, prepare not to be gone;

We have a trifling foolish banquet towards.

Is it e'ven so? Why, then, I thank you all;

I thank you, honest gentlemen; good night.

More torches here! Come on, then, let's to bed.

   *(to second Capulet)*

Ah, sirrah, by my fay, it waxes late:

I'll to my rest.

   *(Exeunt all but Juliet and Nurse)*

**JULIET**

Come hither, nurse. What is yond gentleman?

**NURSE**

The son and heir of old Tiberio.

**JULIET**

What's he that now is going out of door?

**NURSE**

Marry, that, I think, be young Petruchio.

**JULIET**

What's he that follows there, that would not dance?

**NURSE**

I know not.

**JULIET**

Go, ask his name: if he be married,

My grave is like to be my wedding-bed.

**NURSE**

His name is Romeo, and a Montague;

The only son of your great enemy.

**JULIET**

My only love sprung from my only hate!

Too early seen unknown, and known too late!

Prodigious birth of love it is to me,

That I must love a loathed enemy.

*This extract is taken from Act 3 Scene 5 – Juliet says goodbye to Romeo after spending the night with him.*

**JULIET**

Wilt thou be gone? It is not yet near day.

It was the nightingale and not the lark

That pierced the fearful hollow of thine ear.

Nightly she sings on yon pomegranate tree.

Believe me, love, it was the nightingale.

**ROMEO**

It was the lark, the herald of the morn,

No nightingale. Look, love, what envious streaks

Do lace the severing clouds in yonder east.

Night's candles are burnt out, and jocund day

Stands tiptop on the misty mountain tops.

I must be gone and live, or stay and die.

**JULIET**

Yon light is not daylight. I know it, I.

It is some meteor that the sun exhales

To be to thee this night a torchbearer,

And light thee on thy way to Mantua.

Therefore stay yet: though need'st not be gone.

**ROMEO**

Let me be ta'en. Let me be put to death.

I am content, so thou wilt have it so.

I'll say yon grey is not the morning's eye,

'Tis but the pale reflex of Cynthia's brow.

Nor that is not the lark whose notes do beat

The vaulty heaven so high above our heads.

I have more care to stay than will to go.

Come death, and welcome. Juliet wills it so.

How is't, my soul? Let's talk. It is not day.

**JULIET**

It is, it is. Hie hence! Be gone, away!

It is the lark that sings so out of tune,

Straining harsh discords and unpleasing sharps.

Some say the lark makes sweet division.

This doth not so, for she divideth us.

Some say the lark and loathed toad change eyes.

O, now I would they had changed voices too,

Since arm from arm that voice doth us affray,

Hunting thee hence with hunt's-up to the day.

O, now be gone; more light and light it grows.

**ROMEO**

More light and light: more dark and dark our woes.

*(Enter Nurse)*

**NURSE**

Madam.

**JULIET**

Nurse?

**NURSE**

Your lady mother is coming to your chamber.

The day is broke; be wary, look about.

*Exit*

**JULIET**

Then, window, let day in and let life out.

**ROMEO**

Farewell, farewell. One kiss and I'll descend.

*They kiss; Romeo descends.*

**JULIET**

Art thou gone so? Love, lord, ay husband, friend,

I must hear from thee every day in the hour,

For in a minute there are many days.

O, by this count I shall be much in years

Ere I again behold my Romeo.

**ROMEO**

Farewell.

I will omit no opportunity

That may convey my greetings, love, to thee.

**JULIET**

O think'st thou we shall ever meet again?

**ROMEO**

I doubt it not, and all these woes shall serve

For sweet discorses in our times to come.

**JULIET**

O God, I have an ill-divining soul!

Methinks I see thee, now thou art so low,

As one dead in the bottom of a tomb.

Either my eyesight fails, or thou look'st pale.

**ROMEO**

And trust me, love, in my eye so do you.

Dry sorrow drinks our blood. Adieu, adieu.

    *Exit.*

# Othello

## Act 3 Scene 2

*The handkerchief scene.*

## Act 5 Scene 2

*Othello murders Desdemona after Iago's plotting of the handkerchief.*

---

### ESSAY QUESTION

*"Iago is the master of Othello and Desdemona's fate."*

Evaluate this idea by exploring how Othello and Desdemona's relationship breaks down as a consequence of Iago's behaviour.

*Support your points by referring to both extracts.*

<u>You should comment on:</u>

- The language used
- The meaning created
- Representation
- How does Shakespeare want you as the reader to feel?

---

20 marks

*This extract is taken from Act 3 Scene 2 – The handkerchief scene.*

**DESDEMONA**

How now, my dear Othello?

Your dinner and the generous islanders

By you invited, do attend your presence.

**OTHELLO**

I am to blame.

**DESDEMONA**

Why do you speak so faintly?

Are you not well?

**OTHELLO**

I have a pain upon my forehead here.

**DESDEMONA**

Faith, that's with watching; 'twill away again.

Let me but bind it hard, within this hour

It will be well.

**OTHELLO**

Your napkin is too little.

*He puts the handkerchief from him, and she drops it.*

Let it alone. Come, I'll go in with you.

**DESDEMONA**

I am very sorry that you are not well.

*Exeunt Othello and Desdemona*

**EMILIA**

I am glad I have found this napkin:

This was her first remembrance from the Moor.

My wayward husband hath a hundred times

Woo'd me to steal it; but she so loves the token,

For he conjur'd her she should ever keep it,

That she reserves it evermore about her

To kiss and talk to. I'll have the work ta'en out

And give't Iago.

What he will do with it, heaven knows, not I:

I nothing but to please his fantasy.
*Enter Iago*

**IAGO**

How now? What do you here alone?

**EMILIA**

Do not you chide; I have a thing for you.

**IAGO**

You have a thing for me? It is a common thing –

**EMILIA**

Ha!

**IAGO**

To have a foolish wife.

**EMILIA**

O, is that all? What will you give me now for that same handkerchief?

**IAGO**

What handkerchief?

**EMILIA**

What handkerchief!
Why, that the Moor first gave to Desdemona,
That which so often you did bid me steal.

**IAGO**

Hast stolen it from her?

**EMILIA**

No, faith; she let it drop by negligence,
And to th'advantage I being her took't up.
Look, here it is.

**IAGO**

A good wench! Give it me.

**EMILIA**

What will you do with't, that you have been so earnest
To have me filch it?

**IAGO**

*(Snatching it)* Why, what's that to you?

*This extract is taken from Act 5 Scene 2 – Othello murders Desdemona after Iago's plotting of the handkerchief.*

**DESDEMONA**
And have you mercy too! I never did
Offend you in my life; never lov'd Cassio
But with such a general warranty of heaven
As I might love. I never gave him token.

**OTHELLO**
By heaven, I saw my handkerchief in's hand.
O perjur'd woman! Thou dost stone my heart,
And mak'st me call what I intend to do
A murder, which I thought a sacrifice.
I saw the handkerchief.

**DESDEMONA**
He found it then;
I never gave it him. Send for him hither;
Let him confess a truth.

**OTHELLO**
He hath confess'd.

**DESDEMONA**
What, my lord?

**OTHELLO**
That he hath us'd thee.

**DESDEMONA**
How? Unlawfully?

**OTHELLO**
Ay.

**DESDEMONA**
He will not say so.

**OTHELLO**
No, his mouth is stopp'd:
Honest Iago hath ta'en order for't.

**DESDEMONA**

O, my fear interprets! What, is he dead?

**OTHELLO**

Had all his hairs been lives, my great revenge
Had stomach for them all.

**DESDEMONA**

Alas, he is betray'd, and I undone.

**OTHELLO**

Out, strumpet! Weep'st thou for him to my face?

**DESDEMONA**

O banish me, my lord, but kill me not!

**OTHELLO**

Down, strumpet!

**DESDEMONA**

Kill me tomorrow; let me live tonight!

**OTHELLO**

Nay, if you strive –

**DESDEMONA**

But half an hour!

**OTHELLO**

Being done, there is no pause.

**DESDEMONA**

But while I say one prayer!

**OTHELLO**

It is too late.

**DESDEMONA**

O, Lord, Lord, Lord!

*He smothers her.*

# Macbeth

## Act 2 Scene 1

*The dagger hallucination.*

## Act 5 Scene 1

*Lady Macbeth sleepwalks and hallucinates.*

### ESSAY QUESTION

Discuss the importance of deterioration throughout the play. How does the themes of visions, sleep walking and hallucinations play a significant role in the characterisation of Macbeth and Lady Macbeth?

*Support your points by referring to both extracts.*

You should comment on:

- The language used

- The meaning created

- Representation

- How does Shakespeare want you as the reader to feel?

20 marks

*This extract is taken from Act 2 Scene 1 – The dagger hallucination.*

**MACBETH**
Go bid thy mistress, when my drink is ready,
She strike upon the bell. Get thee to bed.
    *Exit servant*
Is this a dagger which I see before me,
The handle toward my hand? Come, let me clutch thee:
I have thee not, and yet I see thee still.
Art thou not, fatal vision, sensible
To feeling as to sight? or art thou but
A dagger of the mind, a false creation,
Proceeding from the heat-oppressed brain?
I see thee yet, in form as palpable
As this which now I draw.
Thou marshall'st me the way that I was going
And such an instrument I was to use.
Mine eyes are made the fools o'th'other senses,
Or else worth all the rest: I see thee still;
And on thy blade and dudgeon gouts of blood,
Which was not so before. – there's no such thing:
It is the bloody business which informs
Thus to mine eyes. – now o'er the one half-world
Nature seems dead, and wicked dreams abuse
The curtain'd sleep; now witchcraft celebrates
Pale Hecate's offerings; and wither'd murder.
Alarum'd by his sentinel, the wolf,
Whose howl's his watch, thus with his stealthy pace,
With Tarquin's ravishing strides, towards his design
Moves like a ghost. – thou sure and firm-set earth,
Hear not my steps, which way they walk, for fear
Thy very stones prate of my whereabout,
And take the present horror from the time

Which now suits with it. – whiles I threat, he lives:
Words to the heat of deeds too cold breath gives.
*A bell rings.*
I go, and it is done; the bell invites me.
Hear it not, Duncan; for it is a knell
That summons thee to heaven or to hell.
*Exit.*

*This extract is taken from Act 5 Scene 1 – Lady Macbeth sleepwalks and hallucinates.*

**DOCTOR**

How came she by that light?

**GENTLEWOMAN**

Why, it stood by her: she has light by her continually; 'tis her command.

**DOCTOR**

You see, her eyes are open.

**GENTLEWOMAN**

Ay, but their sense is shut.

**DOCTOR**

What is it she does now? Look, how she rubs her hands.

**GENTLEWOMAN**

It is an accustom'd action with her, to seem that washing her hands:

I have known her continue in this a quarter of an hour.

**LADY MACBETH**

Yet here's a spot.

**DOCTOR**

Hark! She speaks: I will set down what comes from her, to satisfy my remembrance the more strongly.

**LADY MACBETH**

Out, damned spot! Out, I say! – one, two; why, then 'tis time to do't. – Hell is murky! – Fie, my lord, fie! A soldier, and afeared? What need we fear who knows it, when none can call our power to account? – yet who would have thought the old man to have had so much blood in him?

**DOCTOR**

Do you mark that?

**LADY MACBETH**

The thane of Fife had a wife; where is she now? –

What, will these hands ne'er be clean? – No more o'that, my lord, no more o'that: you mar all with this starting.

**DOCTOR**

Go to, go to; you have known what you should not.

**GENTLEWOMAN**

She has spoke what she should not, I am sure of that: heaven knows what she has known.

**LADY MACBETH**

Here's the smell of the blood still: all the perfumes of Arabia will not sweeten this little hand. Oh, oh, oh!

**DOCTOR**

What a sight is there! The heart is sorely charged.

**GENTLEWOMAN**

I would not have such a heart in my bosom for the dignity of the whole body.

**DOCTOR**

Well, well, well, -

**GENTLEWOMAN**

Pray God it be, sir.

**DOCTOR**

This disease is beyond my practice: yet I have known those which have walkt in their sleep who have died holily in their beds.

**LADY MACBETH**

Wash your hands, put on your nightgown; look not so pale: - I tell you yet again, Banquo's buried; he cannot come out on's grave.

**DOCTOR**

Even so?

**LADY MACBETH**

To bed, to bed; there's knocking at the gate:

Come, come, come, come, give me your hand:

What's done cannot be undone: to bed, to bed, to bed.

   *Exit.*

# KEY STAGE 3 English

# SET A Writing Practice Paper 3

**Questions**

**1 hour 15 minutes**

| | |
|---|---|
| **First Name** | |
| **Middle Name/s** | |
| **Last Name** | |
| **School** | |
| **Date of Birth** | *D D  /  M M  /  Y Y Y Y* |

## Within this paper, you have two exercises:

- Longer writing task
- Shorter writing task

For the longer writing task, you should spend **45 minutes** writing your answer. For this section, you should spend the first 15 minutes planning your answer.

For the shorter writing task, you should spend **30 minutes** writing your answer.

For this paper, there are 50 marks in total:

- 30 marks will be awarded for the longer writing exercise.
- 20 marks will be awarded for the shorter writing exercise.

Make sure you pay attention to grammar, punctuation and spelling. Your writing style will be assessed.

After you've finished writing your answers, have a look at our answer sheet. We have provided you some top tips and things to include in your answer. The answers for Set A Paper 3 can be found on pages 71 – 72.

# Longer Writing Task

You are a journalist working for a major newspaper. You have been informed that a local community is suffering from flash floods.

You receive an email from your boss:

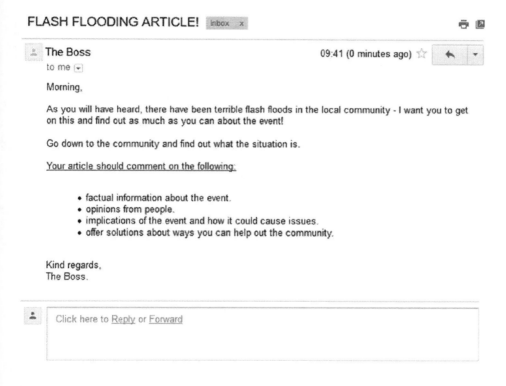

FLASH FLOODING ARTICLE! Inbox x

The Boss — 09:41 (0 minutes ago)
to me

Morning,

As you will have heard, there have been terrible flash floods in the local community - I want you to get on this and find out as much as you can about the event!

Go down to the community and find out what the situation is.

Your article should comment on the following:

- factual information about the event.
- opinions from people.
- implications of the event and how it could cause issues.
- offer solutions about ways you can help out the community.

Kind regards,
The Boss.

Click here to Reply or Forward

**Write your report about the flash floods.**

*You DO NOT need to write in columns. Additional paper may be required.*

30 marks

*Use this page to plan your answer.*

**WHAT HAPPENED?**

**OPINIONS**

**IMPLICATIONS**

**SOLUTIONS**

# Shorter Writing Task

You and your parents are deciding where to go on holiday in the summer. You can't seem to make a unanimous decision in regards to location.

You sit in your bedroom and you decide to write a letter to your parents, persuading them to choose your ideal destination.

In your letter, you should include the following:

- Your ideal destination
- Reasoning for going
- Positives of visiting
- Negatives that you can find in the places they want to go to

Your writing needs to be persuasive. You want to use effective language in order to sway your parents to agree with you.

Remember, you will be marked on grammar, punctuation and spelling.

**Write your letter explaining where you want to go on holiday, and why.**

_You DO NOT need to include an address. Additional paper may be required._

20 marks

# KEY STAGE 3 English

**Total Score**

out of **100**

# SET A
# Answer Booklet

*Answers to Reading, Shakespeare and Writing*

*Using the answers in this booklet, carefully add up the total marks for each paper. The total marks for the **SET** is out of 100.*

*You can use these marks to monitor your child's progression and work on their weaker areas.*

| | READING<br>Mark out of 30 | SHAKESPEARE<br>Mark out of 20 | WRITING<br>Mark out of 50 | TOTAL<br>Mark out of 100 |
|---|---|---|---|---|
| **SET A** | | | | |

# Answers to Set A

## Reading Paper

**Q1.** | **1 mark**

"…and what is the use of a book, without pictures or conversations?"

**Q2.** | **2 marks**
(1 mark for one example. 2 marks for two examples)

Carroll conveys Alice as being conscientious. The first example is when Alice attempts to put the "ORANGE MARMALADE" jar back on the shelf, because she does not want to drop it on anyone underneath her. Secondly, when she thinks about where she might end, she is conscious of the fact that it would be ignorant of her to ask where she is.

**Q3.** | **1 mark**

Carroll repeats the word "wonder" in order to draw upon themes such as curiosity, adventure and wonderment. The narrative is based on Alice's adventures in a world of wonder. Not only that, but it also highlights Alice as being a curious young girl in search of something new.

**Q4.** | **3 marks**
(1 mark for one answer, 2 marks for two answers, 3 marks for three answers)

Simile = "away went Alice like the wind"

Repetition = "wonder"

Rhetorical question = "do you think you could manage it?"

**Q5.** | **3 marks**
(Marks will be awarded for referring to the text, grammar and spelling, and writing ability)

Your answer should include some of the points:

• Curious young girl

What quotes can you find to demonstrate this?

• Content with being on her own

What quotes can you find to demonstrate this?

- Talkative, imaginative, adventurous

What quotes can you find to demonstrate this?

Why do you think the author has conveyed Alice in this way?

## Q6.

| | |
|---|---|
| • "Feed the reindeers"<br><br>• "Santa's grotto"<br><br>*Other answers are applicable. Have someone read through the extract to find your example. It has to be stated in the extract in order for the answer to be correct.* | **1 mark**<br>(The mark can only be awarded if two examples are provided) |

## Q7.

| | |
|---|---|
| Example 1 = "chipmunk-cheeked"<br><br>Example 2 = "carefully crafted"<br><br>Example 3 = "Rudolph's runaway"<br><br>Explanation = alliteration is a great literary technique in order to make the writing sound more rhythmic and appealing. | **2 marks**<br>(1 mark for three examples. 1 mark for a strong explanation) |

## Q8.

| | |
|---|---|
| *This answer is based on your personal feelings.*<br><br>Does the extract make you want to visit? Give reasons for your answer. Make sure you refer back to the text. | **1 mark** |

## Q9.

| | |
|---|---|
| The author begins with a question because it instantly draws the reader in. It makes the text read in a more personal way, which will appeal to the reader and allow them to feel welcome and involved. | **1 mark** |

## Q10.

| | |
|---|---|
| The extract appeals to a wide audience, by stating how there is "something for everyone".<br><br>The language is very persuasive. It caters for all age groups, with a particular focus on kids and families.<br><br>Rhetorical questions are used to draw in the reader and make them want to visit. Alliteration is another great | **5 marks**<br>(Marks will be awarded for establishing an audience, providing reasoning and examples. Marks will also be awarded for grammar, punctuation and spelling) |

technique to make it sound more exciting!

*You should list some of the activities stated, and show how they appeal to a wide group of people. The fact that it's a Christmas event means that most people would enjoy the festivities this has to offer.*

## Q11.

AABB

**1 mark**

The poem uses this rhythmic pattern in order to create a constant beat. Every two lines rhyme, and therefore the use of these rhyming couplets makes the poem read more romantically and happy.

**1 mark**

## Q12.

Rhyming couplet = "10am, the air still **warming**, / That time of year, leaves **transforming**"

**2 marks**

(1 mark for three answers. 2 marks for all six answers)

Colour imagery = "Colours of **yellows**, vibrant and **gold**"

Time imagery = "1 o'clock, strikes"

Repetition = "wonderland"

Simile = "is the freedom I feel; like a flying raven"

Alliteration = "rabbits roaming"

## Q13.

Using a 1st person narration makes the poem more appealing to readers, as they feel they are reading from the perspective of the author. Therefore the reader is able to sympathise and connect with the emotions and feelings of the poet.

**1 mark**

## Q14.

A Garden of Eden symbolises beauty, peace and nature. This is relevant to the narrative of the poem, because the poet often refers to beauty and surrealism. This creates picturesque imagery, which the reader can find idyllic.

**2 marks**

(1 mark for connotation. 1 mark for explaining how this is relevant)

**Q15.**

The poem uses 12 stanzas, each of which represent an hour of time. The first stanza starts at 10am. The fourth stanza is 1 o'clock. This shows how 1 hour has passed from each stanza to the next.

This allows the reader to experience time passing by. The fact that the memories of a wonderland garden are framed by hours passing shows how time flies when one is there. The reader is able to move through time at the same pace as the narrator.

**3 marks**

(1 mark for making a connection about time and stanza. 1 mark for giving reasons why. 1 mark explaining the effect on the reader)

# Shakespeare Paper

*1. What themes are conveyed in these extracts? What do these themes say about the characters of Romeo and Juliet?*

- In Act 1 Scene 5, the first 14 lines of speech between Romeo and Juliet can be read as a sonnet. You can explore how Shakespeare is well known for his poetry, particularly sonnets. The use of a sonnet as a structure of their speech (up until they kiss) suggests the brewing romance between the protagonists.

- Love is also emphasised by key phrases including:

  o "with a tender kiss"

  o "give me my sin again"

- Other themes that are explored include:

  o Religion = the use of the words "sin", "prayer's", "holy" and "saints". Religion is a key theme often explored in Shakespearean literature. The use of religion here suggests that there are rules and boundaries between the characters of Romeo and Juliet. The fact that Romeo states his "unworthiest hand" implies that he is not worthy of the love of Juliet.

  o Secrecy. In Act 3 Scene 5, the scene is set at night. This could be a symbol for the secrecy and forbidden nature of their relationship.

  o Conflict. In the first extract, the fact that Juliet realises her mother would have an issue with her relationship with Romeo, suggests confrontation. In the second extract, Juliet is conflicted with emotions. She wants Romeo to stay because she loves him and has just spent their first night together. However, she also wants him to leave because she knows he is in danger.

  o Desire = "if he be married, / My grave is like to be my wedding-bed"

    "My only love sprung from my only hate"

    "Love, lord, ay husband, friend"

    "O think'st thou we shall ever meet again?"

- What do the themes say about the characters of Romeo and Juliet? How is Juliet represented as being young and naïve? How is Romeo represented as being love-struck and possibly foolish?

- How is their relationship represented? Why do you think Shakespeare has used religious imagery in his writing? What effect would this have on an Elizabethan reader, and a contemporary reader?

**2.** *"Iago is the master of Othello and Desdemona's fate."*
*Evaluate this idea by exploring how Othello and Desdemona's relationship breaks down as a consequence of Iago's behaviour.*

- Iago is the villainous character in *Othello*, and we as the reader witness several attempts to sabotage the relationship of Othello and Desdemona.

- When Desdemona offers her handkerchief to Othello, and he rejects it, this is a clear sign of Iago's cunning plan to convince Othello that his wife has been cheating.

  o *"Your napkin is too little" – He puts the handkerchief from him, and she drops it.* This clearly emphasises their relationship as being in turmoil. The fact that Othello claims the handkerchief is "too little" implies that their relationship is fading.

  o The handkerchief scene in *Othello* is a pivotal scene whereby we witness Iago's behaviour as having a dramatic effect on other characters.

- The fact that Iago then uses the handkerchief to his advantage reinforces how Iago is the master of Othello and Desdemona's fate.

  o When Emilia tells Iago that she has the handkerchief, and asks what he will do with it, the fact that he snatches it from her, and states "why, what's that to you" reinforces that he is up to something.

- In the second extract, Othello confronts Desdemona. The handkerchief again plays a significant role in their breakdown in their relationship – something that was instigated by Iago.

  o "By heaven, I saw my handkerchief in's hand"

  o "O perjur'd woman!"

  o "No, his mouth is stopp'd: / Honest Iago hath ta'en order for't" This ironic statement shows how Othello has fallen for Iago's cunning plans, whilst still remaining trustful in him.

- The reason Othello kills Desdemona is a clear act of jealousy and mistrust. These themes are only stirred in their relationship because of Iago. Without Iago as a villainous character, the reader is led to believe that their relationship could have survived.

- Is Iago completely to blame for the fate of Desdemona and Othello? Or do you think Othello's naivety and trust in Iago is partially to blame for the breakdown in the relationship.

*3.* Discuss the importance of deterioration throughout the play. How does the themes of visions, sleep walking and hallucinations play a significant role in the characterisation of Macbeth and Lady Macbeth?

- In both extracts, we see Macbeth and Lady Macbeth decline as the narrative progresses.

- In the dagger scene, we see Macbeth hallucinate a ghostly dagger. This dagger foreshadows the murder that Macbeth is about to commit in order to become king.

  o "Is this a dagger which I see before me, / The handle toward my hand"

  o "A dagger of the mind, a false creation"

  o "I see before me…I see thee yet…I see thee still"

- Why do you think Shakespeare uses the theme of the supernatural such as hallucinations? What does this say about the role of Macbeth?

- In the second extract, the reader witness Lady Macbeth's character decline. Both her sleep walking and hallucinations reinforces this idea of become mentally unstable, and therefore her powerful character is shown to decline.

  o "Yet here's a spot" – this suggests this idea of blood and how Lady Macbeth is trying to wash away the blood from her hands. Her hands are bloody after the murderous actions both she and Macbeth have involved themselves with.

  o "Will these hands ne'er be clean?" Lady Macbeth is trying to seek forgiveness and wonders whether she will be able to forget about what she has done.

  o "I tell you yet again, / Banquo's buried; he cannot come out on's grave" – this signifies what she has done; she has admitted to murder

- Lady Macbeth's sleep walking and hallucinations put her character in a very vulnerable position. The fact that she is unable to control what she says shows how her character is no longer in control or withholds any power.

- At the time of writing, supernatural was a fascinating topic for the majority of people. Many of the people believed in some form of witchcraft or supernatural element.

- Hallucinations play a crucial role in the play. Both the characters of Macbeth and Lady Macbeth suffer from extreme hallucinations.

- The floating dagger not only illustrates the violence of the play, but also acts as a symbol of Macbeth's guilty conscience. It is a reminder of Macbeth's actions and how this triggers the dramatic events of the narrative.

# Writing Paper

## LONGER WRITING TASK

For the longer writing task, you will be assessed on three main areas:

- Sentence structure, including grammar, punctuation and spelling;
- Text structure and content;
- Composition and effective writing.

For high scores in sentence structure, and grammar, punctuation and spelling:

- Sentence structure is clear and written well.
- You have used a variety of sentence types including subordinate clauses.
- Demonstrate a good use of punctuation, showing that you can use each punctuation mark correctly.
- Emphasise great literary writing by using the correct grammar and spelling. You need to be able to articulate yourself through words, structure and punctuation.

For high scores in text structure and content:

- You have organised and structured writing, using paragraphs when necessary.
- Paragraphs should vary in length depending on the content. Each paragraph should be clearly linked in order for your writing to flow with ease and control.

For high marks in composition and effective writing:

- Your style and tone of writing needs to be suitable in regards to whom you are addressing.
- The content of your writing needs to be relevant to the question being asked.
- Your writing needs to demonstrate the purpose of the text. Is your writing meant to persuade, discuss, analyse or argue?
- Is your writing effective? Is it clear and concise? Is it well structured, well written and relevant?

For Set A Paper 3 (longer writing task):

Your writing needs to emphasise the key points listed in the email including: facts, opinions, implications about the event, and offering resolutions. Your writing needs to be clearly written, with strong use of grammar, punctuation and spelling. You need to demonstrate creative and imaginative thinking, which highlights the key events that is newsworthy.

# SHORTER WRITING TASK

For the shorter writing task, you will be assessed on three main areas:

- Spelling;

- Structure and punctuation;

- Composition and effective writing.

For high scores in spelling:

- Spelling and grammar are used almost always correctly. As a writer, you need to demonstrate strong levels of literary understanding.

For high marks in structure and punctuation:

- Clear understanding of punctuation marks, using a variety of punctuation correctly.

- Demonstrate a strong understanding of structure and the importance this has on written communication.

- Paragraphing is clear in your writing.

- Your paragraphs need to clearly link to one another, and have a clear focus. They also need to be relevant to the topic.

For high marks in composition and effective writing:

- Your style and tone of writing needs to be suitable in regards to whom you are addressing.

- The content of your writing needs to be relevant to the question being asked.

- Your writing needs to demonstrate the purpose of the text. Is your writing meant to persuade, discuss, analyse or argue?

- Is your writing effective? Is it clear and concise? Is it well structured, well written and relevant?

For Set A Paper 3 (shorter writing task):

You need to write a persuasive written piece to convince your parents to go on a holiday destination of your choice. Your writing needs to be written in a mature and convincing way, with strong use of style, grammar and literary techniques. Your writing needs to be original. This writing exercise is not about remembering facts, it's all about opinion. Therefore, you need to emphasise your ideas and opinions, and explain why they are the best choice.

[END OF SET A]

# KEY STAGE 3
## English

**Total Score**

out of **30**

# SET B
# Reading
# Practice Paper 1

**Reading Material & Questions**

1 hour 15 minutes

| First Name | |
|---|---|
| **Middle Name/s** | |
| **Last Name** | |
| **School** | |
| **Date of Birth** | *D D  /  M M  /  Y Y Y Y* |

## Within this paper, you have three extracts:

- Countryside by Day; City by Night
- A Little Princess
- Summer Time Bliss

For each extract, there are 5 questions.

There are 30 marks in total.

Make sure you pay attention to grammar, punctuation and spelling. You will be awarded marks (for the questions with multiple marks on offer) so you don't want to lose out on easy marks.

For this paper, you have 1 hour and 15 minutes. The first 15 minutes should be used to read all of the extracts. The remaining time should be used to answer the questions.

After you've finished the questions, make sure you check your answers. The answers for Set B Paper 1 can be found on pages 120 – 124.

# IMAGINE THE SCENE

Countryside
by Day;
City by Night

A Little Princess

Summer Time
Bliss

## COUNTRYSIDE BY DAY

Deep into the woods, where nothing is heard,
Except for the humming of an invisible bird.
Not a sound, nor whisper, nor spoken word.

An oak tree wrinkled for a 100 years,
The perfect post to shed your tears.
Supportive and strong - like it appears.

Next to the tree flowed a crystal clear stream,
A vision of beauty, a waking dream.
The yellow rays that beat and beamed.

Peaceful bliss, so solitude,
All my thoughts and ideas persued.
A place to think, a place to view.

These are the things the countryside bring,
Butterfly wings and birds that sing.
As precious as a royalty's ring.

High tree tops that offer protection,
A perfect time for self-reflection.
The sounds and wildlife is perfection.

A countryside by day.

## CITY BY NIGHT

Walking along 1st avenue,
The sky above all dark and blue.
Hidden from the colourful lights,
Stars forbidden to shine so bright.

A city of people sleeping away,
Sleeping soundly, awaiting for day.
To me, though, the best part is the night,
Manhattan's magic comes into sight.

A city of life, and a city of beat,
The music that fills the lit-up street.
Never dull, never alone,
Never silent, never a drone.

A city of experience like I have never seen,
The energy, the vibes, the almighty gleam.
Everyone always moving fast-paced,
Yet they move with poise, they move with grace.

The city sounds heard after dark,
Buzzed through the empty, childless park.
Dreams, fantasies and hopes to achieve,
Makes me never want to leave.

A city by night.

77

**Describing Sara Crewe – a young girl from a rich background, sent to boarding school.**

Once on a dark winter's day, when the yellow fog hung so thick and heavy in the streets of London that the lamps were lighted and the shop windows blazed with gas as they do at night, an odd-looking girl sat in a cab with her father and was driven rather slowly through the big thoroughfares.

She sat with her feet tucked under her, and leaned against her father, who held her in his arm, as she stared out of the window at the passing people with a queer old-fashioned thoughtfulness in her big eyes.

She was such a little girl that one did not expect to see such a look on her small face. It would have been an old look for a child of twelve, and Sara Crewe was only seven. The fact was, however, that she was always dreaming and thinking odd things and could not herself remember any time when she had not been thinking things about grown-up people and the world they belonged to. She felt as if she had lived a long, long time.

At this moment she was remembering the voyage she had just made from Bombay with her father, Captain Crewe. She was thinking of the big ship, of the Lascars passing silently to and fro on it, of the children playing about on the hot deck, and of some young officers' wives who used to try to make her talk to them and laugh at the things she said.

Principally, she was thinking of what a queer thing it was that at one time one was in India in the blazing sun, and then in the middle of the ocean, and then driving in a strange vehicle through strange streets where the day was as dark as the night. She found this so puzzling that she moved closer to her father.

"Papa," she said in a low, mysterious little voice which was almost a whisper, "papa."

"What is it, darling?" Captain Crewe answered, holding her closer and looking down into her face. "What is Sara thinking of?"

"Is this the place?" Sara whispered, cuddling still closer to him. "Is it, papa?"

"Yes, little Sara, it is. We have reached it at last." And though she was only seven years old, she knew that he felt sad when he said it.

It seemed to her many years since he had begun to prepare her mind for "the place," as she always called it. Her mother had died when she was born, so she had never known or missed her. Her young, handsome, rich, petting father seemed to be the only relation she had in the world. They had always played together and been fond of each other. She only knew he was rich because she had heard people say so when they thought she was not listening, and she had also heard them say that when she grew up she would be rich, too. She did not know all that being rich meant. She had always lived in a beautiful bungalow, and had been used to seeing many servants who made salaams to her and called her "Missee Sahib," and gave her her own way in everything. She had had toys and pets and an ayah who worshipped her, and she had gradually learned that people who were rich had these things. That, however, was all she knew about it.

**Describing Becky – the scullery maid.**

"Who is the little girl who makes the fires?" she asked Mariette that night.

Mariette broke forth into a flow of description.

Ah, indeed Mademoiselle Sara might well ask. She was a forlorn little thing who had just taken the place of scullery maid – though, as to being scullery maid, she was everything else besides. She blacked boots and grates, and carried heavy coal-scuttles up and down stairs, and scrubbed floors and cleaned windows, and was ordered about by everybody. She was fourteen years old, but was so stunted in growth that she looked about twelve. In truth, Mariette was sorry for her. She was so timid that if one chanced to speak to her it appeared as if her poor, frightened eyes would jump out of her head.

"What is her name?" asked Sara, who had sat by the table, with her chin on her hands, as she listened absorbedly to the recital.

Her name was Becky. Mariette heard everyone below-stairs calling, "Becky, do this," and "Becky, do that," every five minutes in the day.

Sara sat and looked into the fire, reflecting on Becky for some time after Mariette left her. She made up a story of which Becky was the ill-used heroine. She thought she looked as if she had never had quite enough to eat. Her very eyes were hungry. She hoped she should see her again, but though she caught sight of her carrying things up and down stairs on several occasions, she always seemed in such a hurry and so afraid of being seen that it was impossible to speak to her.

But a few weeks later, on another foggy afternoon, when she entered her sitting room she found herself confronting a rather pathetic picture. In her own special and pet easy-chair before the bright fire, Becky – with a coal smudge on her nose and several on her apron, with her poor little cap hanging half off her head, and an empty coal box on the floor near her – sat fast asleep, tired out beyond even the endurance of her hard-working young body. She had been sent up to put the bedrooms in order for the evening. There were a great many of them, and she had been running about all day. Sara's rooms she had saved until the last. They were not like the other rooms, which were plain and bare. Ordinary pupils were expected to be satisfied with mere necessities. Sara's comfortable sitting room seemed a bower of luxury to the scullery maid, though it was, in fact, merely a nice, bright little room. But there were pictures and books in it, and curious things from India; there was a sofa and the low, soft chair; Emily sat in a chair of her own, with the air of a presiding goddess, and there was always a glowing fire and a polished grate. Becky saved it until the end of her afternoon's work, because it rested her to go into it, and she had always hoped to snatch a few minutes to sit down in the sofa chair and look about her, and think about the wonderful good fortune of the child who owned such surroundings and who went out on the cold days in beautiful hats and coats on tried to catch a glimpse of through the area railing.

## *Summer Time Bliss* by How2Become

Over the hill tops, the sun so bright
Beautiful brilliant summer light.
A yellow inferno that warmed the air
Walking the countryside without a care.

Butterfly wings that beat up and down
The perfect time for a cotton, white gown.
Singing, dancing, playing hide 'n' seek
The feeling of reaching mountain peak.

Took my hand, summer romance
Now's the time to take a chance.
A world of love; a world of laughter
Something everyone should lust after.

To think of summer is to captivate
The hidden truths and the hidden fate.
What makes this day truly one of a kind
Is the guy who filled my mind.

Down by the river, we lie side-by-side
Glance over to the guy, blue-eyed.
Here he says those special three words
Amongst the breeze, amongst the birds.

Summer time bliss painted with perfection
Vision of rays, heading in one direction.
Follow your heart and follow your dreams
Whether that small, or whether extreme.

Now's the time to say goodbye
All choked up, all starry-eyed.
The perfect day, the perfect bliss
Ended with true love's first kiss.

**Questions 1 – 5 are for *"Countryside by Day; City by Night"* by How2Become (this extract can be found on page 77 of the reading material).**

⭐1 In 'Countryside by Day', the poet describes a peaceful, idyllic, beautiful atmosphere.

Find two examples from the poem, and describe how they link to themes of beauty and serenity.

**EXAMPLE 1**

_____

_____

**EXAMPLE 2**

_____

_____

2 marks

⭐2 In 'City by Night', the poem describes a very different atmosphere compared to that in 'Countryside by Day'. Find two examples and explain what mood and atmosphere is created.

**EXAMPLE 1**

_____

_____

**EXAMPLE 2**

_____

_____

2 marks

⭐ **3** Read both poems again. Explain why it is more than likely that these poems were written by the same person. Use examples to support your reasoning.

_____

_____

_____

_____

_____

1 mark

⭐ **4** Below is a table. Fill in the table with examples taken from the poems. <u>Both poems may not contain the same literary devices. If so, write "N/A".</u>

|  | COUNTRYSIDE BY DAY | CITY BY NIGHT |
|---|---|---|
| **SIMILE** | | |
| **ALLITERATION** | | |
| **SOUND IMAGERY** | | |
| **RHYMING PATTERNS** | | |
| **ONOMATOPOEIA** | | |
| **OXYMORON** | | |

3 marks

For each poem, 'Countryside by Day' and 'City by Night', you need to create your own stanza.

When creating your stanza (one for 'Countryside by Day' and one for 'City by Night') you should consider the following:

- Language
- Structure
- Rhymes
- Imagery

<br>

**COUNTRYSIDE BY DAY**

<br>

**CITY BY NIGHT**

2 marks

**Questions 6 – 10 are for *"A Little Princess"* by Frances Hodgson Burnett (this extract can be found on pages 78 – 80 of the reading material).**

⭐ **6** What is Sara's perception of London? Use examples from the passage to support your answer.

_____

_____

_____

_____

_____

_____

2 marks

⭐ **7** The theme of memories is apparent in the passage. Using examples, explain why the author has referred to Sara's memories.

What does this say about the character of Sara?

_____

_____

_____

_____

_____

_____

_____

_____

_____

_____

_____

_____

_____

2 marks

Read both passages about Sara and Becky. Compare and contrast the characters of Sara and Becky.

Why do you think the author has created such different characters? What effect does this have on the reader?

<u>When answering this question, you should consider the following:</u>

- Language
- Dress code
- Appearance
- Speech

_____

_____

_____

_____

_____

_____

_____

_____

_____

_____

_____

_____

_____

_____

_____

_____

_____

5 marks

**9** Why do you think Sara leaned closer and closer into her father? What does this suggest about how Sara is feeling?

1 mark

**10** How does the author use language to make Sara's room seem grand and luxurious?

2 marks

Questions 11 – 15 are for *"Summer Time Bliss"* by How2Become (this extract can be found on page 81 of the reading material).

 **11** The poem is written in which narration? <u>Circle</u> **one**.

| 1st PERSON | 2nd PERSON | 3rd PERSON |

Why do you think the poet has chosen to use this narration for their poem?

_____

_____

_____

**1 mark**

**12** Describe the structure and rhythm of the poem.

_____

_____

_____

_____

**2 marks**

**13** Do you think the same structure and rhythm of the poem would work for a narrative based on something serious or sad? Explain your answer.

_____

_____

_____

_____

_____

**2 marks**

**14** How does the poet want you to feel in the last stanza?

1 mark

**15** Write your own stanza to fit in with this poem.

Explain your reasoning for the choice of vocabulary, rhyming pattern and language used.

2 marks

# KEY STAGE 3
## English

# SET B
# Shakespeare
# Practice Paper 2

**Reading Material & Questions**

**45 minutes**

| | |
|---|---|
| **First Name** | |
| **Middle Name/s** | |
| **Last Name** | |
| **School** | |
| **Date of Birth** | D D / M M / Y Y Y Y |

## Within this paper, you have three plays:

- Romeo and Juliet

- Othello

- Macbeth

For each play, there are two extracts. There is one essay to answer based on each play.

**I would recommend you study the extracts that you are learning in the classroom**. If these are different, then practise using these to better your understanding of Shakespearean language.

There are 20 marks in total. **Answer only ONE essay question.**

Make sure you pay attention to grammar, punctuation and spelling. Your writing style will be assessed.

For this paper, you have 45 minutes. The first 15 minutes should be used to plan your essay. The remaining time should be used to write your essay.

After you've finished the questions, make sure you check your answers. The answers for Set B Paper 2 can be found on pages 125 – 127.

# SHAKESPEARE

Romeo
and Juliet

Othello

Macbeth

# Romeo and Juliet

## Act 3 Scene 1

*Romeo kills Tybalt.*

## Act 5 Scene 3

*Romeo dies.*

---

### ESSAY QUESTION

Analyse the theme of death and love in relation to characters, motif, and narrative. Why are these death scenes important to the play of *Romeo and Juliet*?

Pay attention to familial, political, moral and personal issues.

*Support your points by referring to both extracts.*

You should comment on:

- The language used
- The meaning created
- Representation
- How does Shakespeare want you as the reader to feel?

---

20 marks

*This extract is taken from Act 3 Scene 1 – Romeo kills Tybalt.*

**ROMEO**

This gentleman, the Prince's near ally,

My very friend, hath got his mortal hurt

In my behalf. My reputation stained

With Tybalt's slander. – Tybalt, that an hour

Hath been my kinsman! O sweet Juliet,

Thy beauty hath made me effeminate

And in my temper softened valor's steel.

*Enter Benvolio*

**BENVOLIO**

O Romeo, Romeo, brave Mercutio is dead!

That gallant spirit hath aspired the clouds,

Which too untimely here did scorn the earth.

**ROMEO**

This day's black fate on more days doth depend.

This but begins the woe others must end.

*Enter Tybalt.*

**BENVOLIO**

Here comes the furious Tybalt back again.

**ROMEO**

Alive in triumph – and Mercutio slain!

Away to heaven, respective lenity,

And fire-eyed fury be my conduct now.

Now, Tybalt, take the "villain" back again

That late thou gavest me, for Mercutio's soul

Is but a little way above our heads,

Staying for thine to keep him company.

Either thou or I, or both, must go with him.

**TYBALT**

Thou, wretched boy, that didst consort him here

Shalt with him hence.

**ROMEO**

This shall determine that.

*They fight. Tybalt falls.*

**BENVOLIO**

Romeo, away, be gone!

The citizens are up, and Tybalt slain.

Stand not amazed. The Prince will doom thee death

If thou art taken. Hence, be gone, away!

**ROMEO**

Oh, I am fortune's fool!

**BENVOLIO**

Why dost thou stay?

*Exit Romeo.*

*This extract is taken from Act 5 Scene 3 – Romeo dies.*

*Romeo opens the tomb to reveal Juliet inside*

**ROMEO**

A grave? Oh no. A lantern slaughtered youth,

For here lies Juliet, and her beauty makes

This vault a feasting presence full of light.

Death, lie thou there, by a dead man interred.

*Lays Paris in the tomb*

How oft when men are at the point of death

Have they been merry, which their keepers call

A lightning before death! Oh, how may I

Call this a lightning? – O my love, my wife!

Death, that hath sucked the honey of thy breath,

Hath had no power yet upon thy beauty.

Thou art not conquered. Beauty's ensign yet

Is crimson in thy lips and in thy cheeks,

And death's pale flag is not advanced there.

Tybalt, liest thou there in thy bloody sheet?

O, what more favour can I do to thee,

Than with that hand that cut thy youth in twain

To sunder his that was thine enemy?

Forgive me, cousin. – Ah dear, Juliet,

Why art thou yet so fair? Shall I believe

That unsubstantial death is amorous,

And that the lean abhorred monster keeps

Thee here in dark to be his paramour?

For fear of that, I still will stay with thee,

And never from this palace of dim night

Depart again. Here, here I will remain

With worms that are thy chamber maids. Oh, here

Will I set up my everlasting rest,

And shake the yoke of inauspicious stars

From this world-wearied flesh. Eyes, look your last.
Arms, take your last embrace. And lips, O you
The doors of breath, seal with a righteous kiss
A dateless bargain to engrossing death.

*Kisses Juliet, takes out the poison*

Come, bitter conduct, come, unsavoury guide.
Thou desperate pilot, now at once run on
The dashing rocks thy seasick, weary bark.
Here's to my love!

*Drinks the poison*

O true apothecary,
Thy drugs are quick. Thus with a kiss I die.

*Romeo dies*

# Othello

## Act 4 Scene 3

*Desdemona and Emilia are talking.*

## Act 5 Scene 2

*Emilia realises Desdemona is dead.*

---

### ESSAY QUESTION

*"Shakespeare's play Othello presents us with a very limited view of women."* Discuss.

Explore the representation of women in the play, and how they are subject to a male hierarchy. Why is this important to both an Elizabethan and contemporary reader?

*Support your points by referring to both extracts.*

You should comment on:

- The language used
- The meaning created
- Representation
- How does Shakespeare want you as the reader to feel?

20 marks

**DESDEMONA**

I have heard it said so. O, these men, these men!

Dost thou in conscience think – tell me, Emilia –

That there be women do abuse their husbands in such gross kind?

**EMILIA**

There be some such, no question.

**DESDEMONA**

Wouldst thou do such a deed for all the world?

**EMILIA**

Why, would not you?

**DESDEMONA**

No, by this heavenly light.

**EMILIA**

Nor I neither by this heavenly light;

I might do's as well i'th'dark.

**DESDEMONA**

Wouldst thou do such a deed for all the world?

**EMILIA**

The world's a huge thing; it is a great price

For a small vice.

**DESDEMONA**

In troth, I think thou wouldst not.

**EMILIA**

In troth, I think I should, and undo't when I had done it. Marry, I would not do such a thing for a joint-ring, nor for measures of lawn, nor for gowns, petticoats, nor caps, nor any petty exhibition. But for all the whole world! Ud's pity, who would not make her husband a cuckold, to make him a monarch? I should venture purgatory for't.

**DESDEMONA**

Beshrew me, if I would do such a wrong for the whole world.

**EMILIA**

Why, the wrong is but a wrong I'th'world; and having the world for your labour, 'tis a wrong in your own world, and you might quickly make it right.

**DESDEMONA**

I do not think there is any such woman.

**EMILIA**

Yes, a dozen; and as many to th'advantage as would store the world they played for.

But I do think it is their husband' faults

If wives do fall. Say that they slack their duties

And pour our treasures into foreign laps,

Or else break out in peevish jealousies,

Throwing restraint upon us; or say they strike us,

Or scant our former having in despite –

Why, we have galls, and though we have some grace,

Yet have we some revenge. Let husbands know

Their wives have sense like them: they see, and smell,

And have their palates both for sweet and sour

As husbands have. What is it that they do

When they change us for others? Is it sport?

I think it is. And doth affection breed it?

I think it doth. Is't frailty that thus errs?

It is so too. And have not we affections,

Desires for sport, and frailty, as men have?

Then let them use us well; else let them know

The ills we do, their ills instruct us so.

**DESDEMONA**

Good night, good night. God me such uses send,

Not to pick bad from bad, but by bad mend!

   *Exit.*

*This extract is taken from Act 5 Scene 2 – Emilia realises Desdemona is dead.*

**OTHELLO**

Yes – 'tis Emilia – by and by. – She's dead.

'Tis like she comes to speak of Cassio's death:

The noise was high. Ha! No more moving?

Still as the grave. Shall she come in? Were't good?

I think she stirs again. No. what's best to do?

If she come in, she'll sure speak to my wife –

My wife, my wife! What wife? I have no wife –

O insupportable! O heavy hour!

Methinks it should be now a huge eclipse

Of sun and moon , and that th'affrighted globe

Should yawn at alteration.

**EMILIA**

*(Within)* I do beseech you

That I may speak with you. O, good my lord!

**OTHELLO**

I had forgot thee. O, come in, Emilia.

Soft, by and by. Let me the curtains draw.

Where art thou?

   *He unlocks the door.*

What's the matter with thee now?

   *Enter Emilia*

**EMILIA**

O, my good lord, yonder's foul murders done.

**OTHELLO**

What? Now?

**EMILIA**

But now, my lord.

**OTHELLO**

It is the very error of the moon:

She comes more nearer earth than she was wont
And makes men mad.

**EMILIA**

Cassio, my lord, hath kill'd a young Venetian
Called Roderigo.

**OTHELLO**

Roderigo kill'd?
And Cassio kill'd?

**EMILIA**

No, Cassio is not kill'd.

**OTHELLO**

Not Cassio kill'd! then murder's out of tune,
And sweet revenge grows harsh.

**DESDEMONA**

O, falsely, falsely murder'd!

**EMILIA**

O Lord! What cry is that?

**OTHELLO**

That? What?

**EMILIA**

Out and alas, that was my lady's voice!

*She draws the bed-curtains*

Help, help, ho, help! O, lady, speak again!
Sweet Desdemona, O sweet mistress, speak!

**DESDEMONA**

A guiltless death I die.

**EMILIA**

O, who hath done this deed?

**DESDEMONA**

Nobody; I myself. Farewell.
Commend me to my kind lord. O farewell!

*She dies*

# Macbeth

## Act 1 Scene 3

*The witches visit Macbeth.*

## Act 4 Scene 1

*The witches return to Macbeth.*

---

### ESSAY QUESTION

**Agree or disagree:** the role of the witches play a significant role in *Macbeth*.

*Support your points by referring to both extracts.*

<u>You should comment on:</u>

- The language used
- The meaning created
- Representation
- How does Shakespeare want you as the reader to feel?

---

20 marks

*This extract is taken from Act 1 Scene 3 – the witches visit Macbeth.*

**MACBETH**

Speak, if you can: what are you?

**FIRST WITCH**

All hail, Macbeth! Hail to thee, thane of Glamis!

**SECOND WITCH**

All hail, Macbeth! Hail to thee, thane of Cawdor!

**THIRD WITCH**

All hail, Macbeth, that shalt be king hereafter!

**BANQUO**

Good sir, why do you start and seem to fear

Things that do sound so fair?

   *(to the witches)*

I' th' name of truth,

Are ye fantastical, or that indeed

Which outwardly ye show? My noble partner

You greet with present grace and great prediction

Of noble having and of royal hope,

That he seems rapt withal. To me you speak not.

If you can look into the seeds of time

And say which grain will grow and which will not,

Speak, then, to me, who neither beg nor fear

Your favors nor your hate.

**FIRST WITCH**

Hail!

**SECOND WITCH**

Hail!

**THIRD WITCH**

Hail!

**FIRST WITCH**

Lesser than Macbeth and greater.

**SECOND WITCH**

Not so happy, yet much happier.

**THIRD WITCH**

Thou shalt get kings, though thou be none.

So all hail, Macbeth and Banquo!

**FIRST WITCH**

Banquo and Macbeth, all hail!

**MACBETH**

Stay, you imperfect speakers, tell me more.

By Sinel's death I know I am thane of Glamis.

But how of Cawdor? The thane of Cawdor lives,

A prosperous gentleman, and to be king

Stands not within the prospect of belief,

No more than to be Cawdor. Say from whence

You owe this strange intelligence, or why

Upon this blasted heath you stop our way

With such prophetic greeting. Speak, I charge you.

*Witches vanish*

This extract is taken from Act 4 Scene 1 – the witches return to Macbeth.

*Thunder. First apparition: an armed head*

**MACBETH**

Tell me, thou unknown power -

**FIRST WITCH**

He knows thy thought.

Hear his speech but say thou nought.

**FIRST APPARITION**

Macbeth! Macbeth! Macbeth! Beware Macduff.

Beware the thane of Fife. Dismiss me. Enough.

*Descends*

**MACBETH**

Whate'er thou art, for thy good caution, thanks.

Thou hast harped my fear alright. But one word more –

**FIRST WITCH**

He will not be commanded. Here's another

More potent than the first.

*Thunder. Second apparition: a bloody child*

**SECOND APPARITION**

Macbeth! Macbeth! Macbeth! –

**MACBETH**

Had I three ears, I'd hear thee.

**SECOND APPARITION**

Be bloody, bold, and resolute. Laugh to scorn

The power of man, for none of woman born

Shall harm Macbeth.

*Descends*

**MACBETH**

Then live, Macduff. What need I fear of thee?

But yet I'll make assurance double sure,

And take a bond of fate. Thou shalt not live,

That I may tell pale-hearted fear it lies,

And sleep in spite of thunder.

*Thunder. Third apparition: a child crowned, with a tree in his hand*

What is this

That rises like the issue of a king,

And wears upon his baby-brow the round

And top of sovereignty?

**ALL**

Listen but speak not 't.

**THIRD APPARITION**

Be lion-mettled, proud, and take no care

Who chafes, who frets, or where conspirers are.

Macbeth shall never vanquished be until

Great Birnam Wood to high Dunsinane Hill

Shall come against him.

*Descends*

**MACBETH**

That will never be.

Who can impress the forest, bid the tree

Unfix his earthbound root? Sweet bodements!

Good!

Rebellious dead, rise never till the wood

Of Birnam rise, and our high-placed Macbeth

Shall live the lease of nature, pay his breath

To time and mortal custom. Yet my heart

Throbs to know one thing. Tell me, if your art

Can tell so much: shall Banquo's issue ever

Reign in this kingdom?

**ALL**

Seek to know no more.

**MACBETH**

I will be satisfied. Deny me this,

And an eternal curse fall on you! Let me kno.

Why sinks that cauldron? And what noise is this?

# KEY STAGE 3
## English

**Total Score**

out of **50**

# SET B
# Writing
# Practice Paper 3

## Questions
## 1 hour 15 minutes

| First Name | |
|---|---|
| Middle Name/s | |
| Last Name | |
| School | |
| Date of Birth | *D D  /  M M  /  Y Y Y Y* |

## Within this paper, you have two exercises:

- Longer writing task
- Shorter writing task

For the longer writing task, you should spend **45 minutes** writing your answer. For this section, you should spend the first 15 minutes planning your answer.

For the shorter writing task, you should spend **30 minutes** writing your answer.

For this paper, there are 50 marks in total:

- 30 marks will be awarded for the longer writing exercise.
- 20 marks will be awarded for the shorter writing exercise.

Make sure you pay attention to grammar, punctuation and spelling. Your writing style will be assessed.

After you've finished writing your answers, have a look at our answer sheet. We have provided you some top tips and things to include in your answer. The answers for Set B Paper 3 can be found on pages 128 – 129.

# Longer Writing Task

You are entering a writing competition.

Role models are extremely important for the younger generation. Young people admire and look up to other people.

Write about your role model. This can be someone famous or a person you know.

You should focus on the following points:

- Give background information about that person;
- What makes them inspirational;
- What do you admire;

You should make sure your language is clear and focused. Marks will be awarded for grammar, punctuation and spelling.

**Write your essay.**

*Additional paper may be required.*

30 marks

**PLAN:**

# Shorter Writing Task

You are applying for a summer job as a holiday rep at a holiday park abroad.

You know that many people your age will be applying for the same job you are. Therefore, you need to make your application stand out.

In your application you should consider the following:

- Why do you want to apply for the job?
- What are your strengths?
- What makes you better than other candidates who have applied?

The job specification requires:

- Fun, outgoing enthusiastic individuals;
- Reliable, hard-working and motivated people;
- Great communication skills;
- Creative thinking and an ability to think of new games and activities.

**Write your application form for the job**.

*We have started your application form for you. Additional paper may be required.*

20 marks

Dear Mr Adams,

I am writing this application for the position of holiday rep at your holiday park.

# KEY STAGE 3 English

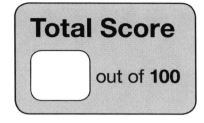

**Total Score**

out of **100**

# SET B
# Answer Booklet

*Answers to Reading, Shakespeare and Writing*

*Using the answers in this booklet, carefully add up the total marks for each paper. The total marks for the **SET** is out of 100.*

*You can use these marks to monitor your child's progression and work on their weaker areas.*

|  | READING<br>Mark out of 30 | SHAKESPEARE<br>Mark out of 20 | WRITING<br>Mark out of 50 | TOTAL<br>Mark out of 100 |
|---|---|---|---|---|
| **SET B** |  |  |  |  |

# Answers to Set B

## Reading Paper

**Q1.**

Example 1 = "Next to the tree flowed a crystal clear stream, / A vision of beauty, a waking dream". This quote from the poem demonstrates the beauty and nature of the countryside. It represents serenity and tranquillity. The 'crystal clear stream' connotes peacefulness.

Example 2 = "The sounds and wildlife is perfection". Again, the poet uses sound imagery alongside the beauty of the nature and wildlife to demonstrate the beauty and idyllic setting of the countryside.

**2 marks**
(1 mark for one example)

**Q2.**

Example 1 = "The music that fills the lit-up street". This creates a very different mood and atmosphere compared to the other poem. This shows a vibrant city, full of life.

Example 2 = "Never dull, never alone, / Never silent, never a drone". Again this quote creates an upbeat vibe of a city that is always on the go.

**2 marks**
(1 mark for one example)

**Q3.**

The poems 'Countryside by Day' and 'City by Night' seem to be written by the same poet. The poems both use similar language and rhythm in order to carry the narrative. All of the stanzas use rhyming last words, which again shows a similar pattern. For example, in the first poem, the words "heard", "bird" and "word" rhyme. In the second poem, the words "avenue" and "blue", and "lights" and "bright" rhyme.

Both poems also focus on the good things about night and day. They both have a hopeful tone; neither is pessimistic.

Another reason which suggests that the poems were written by the same person, is how the poems end. Both poems end with one final line – "a countryside by day" and "a city by night".

**1 mark**

| | |
|---|---|
| **Q4.** | **3 marks** |
| **Simile =** | (3 marks for six answers. |
| "As precious as a royalty's ring" | 2 marks for four or five. |
| N/A | 1 mark for three or less |
| **Alliteration** | answers) |
| "Crystal clear" | |
| "Sleeping soundly" | |
| **Sound imagery** | |
| "Not a sound, nor whisper, nor spoken word" | |
| "The music that fills the lit-up sky" | |
| **Rhyming patterns** | |
| "Heard" "bird" "word" | |
| "Away" "day" | |
| **Onomatopoeia** | |
| N/A | |
| "Buzzed" | |
| **Oxymoron** | |
| "A waking dream" | |
| N/A | |
| | |
| **Q5.** | **2 marks** |
| *This is based on your own creative writing. You need to write one stanza for 'Countryside by Day' and one stanza for 'City by Night'.* | (1 mark for each stanza that demonstrates similar features as the poem) |
| *Marks will be awarded for language, structure, rhymes and imagery.* | |
| *Have someone read your stanza, and see whether you have used similar features as the poet.* | |
| | |
| **Q6.** | **2 marks** |
| Sara's perception of London appears to be quite reserved and intimated. The fact that Sara sits with "her feet tucked under her, and leaned against her father, who held her in his arm" suggests that she is scared. She describes London as being "strange". It is much different to the world she comes from, and therefore the idea of living here seems to daunt her. | (1 mark for describing London, and 1 mark for using examples) |

**Q7.**

Memories is a key theme in the extracts provided. The fact that Sara recalls her dead mother, and where she used to live, suggests that she is holding on to her past.

"At this moment she was remembering the voyage she had just made from Bombay with her father". This suggests how Sara is not only a young girl, but also shows that she relies on her memories to live in the present.

**2 marks**

(Award 2 marks for outlining the importance of memories and how this adds character to Sara)

**Q8.**

The character of Sara is represented as being a young, rich girl who has experienced a great deal of life and adventure. In comparison to the "scullery maid", Becky is described as the exact opposite to her. Oppositions between these two characters go beyond clothes, language, and appearance, but how young girls are treated based on wealth.

Becky has very little to say in the extract, and is represented as being a very shy, timid girl. Whereas Sara is an extremely vocal character who demonstrates confidence.

Quotations to consider:

*   "She had always lived in a beautiful bungalow, and had been used to seeing many servants"
*   "She had had toys and pets and an ayah who worshipped her"
*   "Mademoiselle Sara"
*   "She was fourteen years old, but was so stunted in growth that she look about twelve"
*   "think about the wonderful good fortune of the child who owned such surroundings and who went out on the cold days in beautiful hats and coats"

**5 marks**

(Marks to be awarded for comparison, description, analysis and examples)

**Q9.**

Sarah "leaned against her father" to not only show that she is a young child who is comforted by her father's presence, but also that she is uncertain and scared of the new adventure that she's about to embark upon.

**1 mark**

**Q10.**

The author makes Sara's room seem grand and luxurious through descriptive writing. Sara's room is described as being unlike "the other rooms, which were plain and bare". The fact that Sara's room was filled with "pictures and books…and curious things from India" reinforces how luxurious her room was – certainly for a "scullery maid" to experience for the first time.

**2 marks**

(1 mark for describing Sara's room, and 1 mark for using examples)

**Q11.**

1st person

The poem is written in 1st person, and is demonstrated through the use of the word "my". The poet uses this narration because it makes the reader read the poem, as if it's an account of the poet. This makes the poem more personal.

**1 mark**

**Q12.**

The structure of the poem is written in 7 stanzas, of four lines each. The rhythm of this poem follows an AABB rhyme scheme. For example, in the first stanza, the first and second lines rhyme with the words "bright" and "light". The third and fourth lines rhyme with the words "air" and "care".

**2 marks**

(1 mark for outlining the structure, and 1 mark for highlighting the rhyming pattern)

**Q13.**

The rhythm of the poem does not fit well with a narrative of sadness or serious topics. The rhythm is quite upbeat and vibrant – it ties in perfectly with a poem about love. This rhythm would be too upbeat for a poem that required a more serious tone.

**2 marks**

(2 marks for reasoning and justification)

**Q14.**

The poet uses the last stanza to draw on a close of summer romance. Although the memory of a true love's kiss remains, the fact that they are saying goodbye, allows the reader to feel sadness. However, the poet still finishes the poem in a happy way, and therefore the reader should still be feeling a sense of romance and happiness.

**1 mark**

**Q15.**

*This requires you to write your own stanza. Remember to use a similar structure and rhyming pattern as the poet. The stanza has to fit in with the rest of the narrative and theme of the poem.*

*Explain why you choose certain words, why you choose the rhyming pattern and language.*

**2 marks**

(Award 1 mark for writing the stanza that fits well with the poem. Award 1 mark for explaining their reasons)

# Shakespeare Paper

*1.* *Analyse the theme of death and love in relation to characters, motif and narrative.* *Why are these death scenes important to the play of Romeo and Juliet? Pay attention* *to familial, political, moral and personal issues.*

- Love and death are two themes that can be closely linked. Both of which play a pivotal role in the inevitable fate of the two protagonists, Romeo and Juliet.

- In Act 3 Scene 1, Romeo kills Tybalt. Not only does this introduce the theme of death, but also sparks family issues.

  o Tybalt is Juliet's cousin. The fact that Romeo has just killed him means that this is going to stir even more conflict between his family and the Capulets.

  o "Brave Mercutio is dead!"

  o "Alive in triumph – and Mercutio slain!"

  o *They fight. Tybalt falls*

  o In a political sense, revenge of killing a family member was considered the norm, and therefore is ironic that Juliet remains loyal to Romeo instead of her family.

- In Act 5 Scene 3, Romeo finds Juliet lying down, presumptuously dead.

- The fact that Romeo kills himself after establishing that his love is dead, clearly shows the strong, powerful love these characters had for one another.

- The true love that Romeo and Juliet feel for one another is linked to their inevitable deaths.

- It is only through the theme of death that Romeo and Juliet are able to preserve their love, and be together.

  o "For here lies Juliet, and her beauty makes"

  o "A lightning before death! Oh, how may I / Call this a lightning? – O my love, my wife!"

  o "Death, that hath sucked the honey of thy breath"

  o "Eyes, look your last. Arms, take your last embrace. And lips, O you / The doors of breath, seal with a righteous kiss"

  o "Here's to my love…thy drugs are quick. Thus with a kiss I die"

Things to consider:

- Do you think the deaths of Romeo and Juliet are inevitable?

- What family, political and morale issues are established within these extracts? What do these say about different characters?

**2.** *"Shakespeare's play Othello presents us with a very limited view of women."*
*Discuss.*

- In the play, there are very few women characters. Apart from Desdemona, Emilia and Bianca are the only other female characters.
    - Why do you think Shakespeare has chosen to show a few women in this play?
    - How effective is this for an Elizabethan audience?
    - What does this say about how times have changed between when the play was written, to today's society?

- In Act 4 Scene 3, Emilia clearly demonstrates her views regarding marriage and the power of men.
    - "I do think it is their husbands' faults / If wives do fall"
    - "Let husbands know / Their wives have sense like them, they see, and smell, / And have their palates both for sweet and sour / As husbands have"
    - Emilia is standing up for women's rights. She states how women have just as much of an equal right to cheat on men, as men do women.

- In Act 5 Scene 2, despite Othello accusing Desdemona of cheating, she still remains loyal and loving until he kills her.
    - "O, falsely, falsely murder'd!"
    - "A guiltless death I die"
    - When asking who did this her, Desdemona responds: "Nobody: I myself" – This suggests that even after Othello has done in regards to his accusations and killing her, she still wants to protect him.

- Shakespeare uses the character of Desdemona to reveal how men distrust women, and how equal rights between men and women had not been established.

- Despite Emilia having reservations and doubts about her husband, Iago, she still remains loyal to him. However, she is a pivotal character in the play, as her monologue suggests that she thinks independently and is profoundly critical of all men.

- Submissiveness is a key motif for *Othello*. Desdemona is conveyed as being obedient and faithful, even when she is being accused. Even in her final breath, she remains dutiful to her husband: "Commend me to my kind lord".

- Although the women are often subjects to a patriarchal society, the female characters are still represented as possessing some levels of authority and power. Emilia is very strong-minded and argues how women are just the same as men. Her monologue is a powerful speech, which allows the reader to explore women as possessing more power than actually shown.

**3. Agree or disagree:** *the role of the witches play a significant role in Macbeth.*

- There is no right or wrong answer for this – you can either agree or disagree with the statement so long as you have reasoning and justification.

- In Act 1 Scene 3, the witches speak to Macbeth regarding their premonitions of what is to occur in the future.

  o The first witch hails Macbeth – "thane of Glamis"

  o The second witch hails Macbeth – "thane of Cawdor"

  o The third witch hails Macbeth – "king hereafter"

- These premonitions could be described as the fundamental reasoning for Macbeth's (and other vital characters') downfall.

- In this Act, the witches also tell Banquo that he will "get kings". I.e. his son will become king.

- Again, this implies that the witches have provided knowledge that subsequently leads to the rest of the action of the play.

- In Act 4 Scene 1, the witches return to Macbeth to provide further future premonitions.

- The use of the apparitions of ghostlike people ties in with the eerie atmosphere and highlights what's to come in the future.

- The use of the "thunder" not only works well with the eerie and ghostly imagery, but it also suggests conflict and battle.

Without the witches, do you think the play would still have turned out in the same way? Do you think the witches were the sole purpose of Macbeth's death?

Quotations to consider:

- "Beware Macduff"

- *Second apparition: a bloody child*

- "Thou shalt get kings, though thou be none. / So all hail, Macbeth and Banquo!"

- "Thou hast harped my fear alright"

Things to consider:

- The role of the apparitions with the witches demonstrates how the future plays a significant role in the events that happen throughout the play of *Macbeth*.

- The witches' apparitions push Macbeth into thinking that Macduff needs to be dealt with. The use of the bloody child as an apparition suggests that Macduff must be murdered.

# Writing Paper

## LONGER WRITING TASK

For the longer writing task, you will be assessed on three main areas:

- Sentence structure, and grammar, punctuation and spelling;
- Text structure and content;
- Composition and effective writing.

For high scores in sentence structure, and grammar, punctuation and spelling:

- Sentence structure is clear and written well.
- You have used a verity of sentence type including subordinate clauses.
- Demonstrated a good use of punctuation, showing that you can use each punctuation mark correctly.
- Emphasised great literary writing by using the correct grammar and spelling. You need to be able to articulate yourself through words, structure and punctuation.

For high scores in text structure and content:

- You have organised and structured writing, using paragraphs when necessary.
- Paragraphs should vary in length depending on the content. Each paragraph should be clearly linked in order for your writing to flow with ease and control.

For high marks in composition and effective writing:

- Your style and tone of writing needs to be suitable in regards to who your writing is addressing.
- The content of your writing needs to be relevant to the question being asked.
- Your writing needs to demonstrate the purpose of the text. Is your writing meant to persuade, discuss, analyse or argue?
- Is your writing effective? Is it clear and concise? Is it well structured, well written and relevant?

For Set B Paper 3 (longer writing task):

Your writing needs to show reasoning and justification as to why you have chosen your role model. Your writing needs to be descriptive, and demonstrate why that person is an inspiration to you. This writing task does not require you to argue or debate anything; it is simply reflecting on your personal beliefs.

# SHORTER WRITING TASK

For the shorter writing task, you will be assessed on three main areas:

- Spelling;
- Structure and punctuation;
- Composition and effective writing.

For high scores in spelling:

- Spelling and grammar, are used almost always correctly. As a writer, you need to demonstrate strong levels of literary understanding.

For high marks in structure and punctuation:

- Clear understanding of punctuation marks, using a variety of punctuation correctly.
- Demonstrate a strong understanding of structure and the importance this has on written communication.
- Paragraphing is clear in your writing.
- Your paragraphs need to clearly link to one another, and have a clear focus. They also need to be relevant to the topic.

For high marks in composition and effective writing:

- Your style and tone of writing needs to be suitable in regards to who your writing is addressing.
- The content of your writing needs to be relevant to the question being asked.
- Your writing needs to demonstrate the purpose of the text. Is your writing meant to persuade, discuss, analyse or argue?
- Is your writing effective? Is it clear and concise? Is it well structured, well written and relevant?

For Set B Paper 3 (shorter writing task):

You need to write a persuasive written application form to convince the holiday park to hire you as a holiday rep for the summer. Your writing needs to be written in a mature and convincing way, with strong use of style, grammar and literary techniques. Your writing needs to be original. This writing exercise is all about selling yourself and making sure you include personal attributes, qualifications and experience in order to highlight your key qualities, and what you can bring to the role.

[END OF SET B]

# NEED A LITTLE EXTRA HELP WITH KEY STAGE 3 (KS3) ENGLISH?

How2Become have created other FANTASTIC guides to help you and your child prepare for Key Stage Three (KS3) English.

These exciting guides are filled with fun and interesting facts for your child to engage with to ensure that their revision is fun, and their learning is improved! Invest in your child's future today!

**FOR MORE INFORMATION ON OUR KEY STAGE 3 (KS3) GUIDES, PLEASE CHECK OUT THE FOLLOWING:**

# WWW.HOW2BECOME.COM

# Get Access To

# FREE

# Psychometric
# Tests

**www.PsychometricTestsOnline.co.uk**

Printed in Great Britain
by Amazon